YOU'RE THE V...
Norah Jones

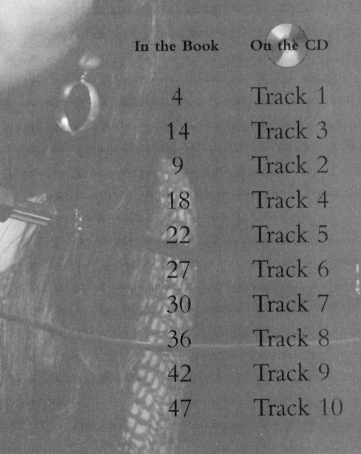

IMP

International
MUSIC
Publications

© International Music Publications Limited
Griffin House 161 Hammersmith Road London W6 8BS England

Editorial, arranging, engraving and recording Artemis Music Limited (www.artemismusic.com)
Design: IMP Studio
Photography: Jim Sharpe / Redferns Music Picture Library

Published 2004

International
MUSIC
Publications

© International Music Publications Limited
Griffin House 161 Hammersmith Road London W6 8BS England

Norah Jones
Born 30th March 1979

The daughter of the renowned Ravi Shankar, Norah Jones was born in New York city and moved, aged four, with her mother Sue Jones to a suburb of Dallas, Texas. Her early musical influences were based on her mother's LP collection, including an eight-album Billie Holiday set – *You Go To My Head* being her favourite.

She started piano lessons around the age of seven, and at 15 enrolled at the Booker T. Washington High School for the Performing and Visual Arts, following this a year later with her first gig at a local coffee-house singing *I'll Be Seeing You*. Year-on-year accolades as Best Jazz Vocalist in the Down Beat Student Music Awards came her way whilst still at high school and she also won Best Original Composition in 1996.

Norah then moved on to major in jazz piano at the University of North Texas and whilst there accepted the offer of a sublet in Greenwich Village in the summer of 1999. This inspired her to write her own songs, leading to a decision not to return to University, and the formation of her own group based around Jesse Harris, Lee Alexander and Dan Rieser. About a year later the group recorded some demos for Blue Note, the tracks impressing the label so much that Jones signed to them in 2001. The album *Come Away With Me* was released early in 2002 and immediately caught the attention of a broad spectrum of the record-buying public, so much so that it eventually went multi-platinum with sales in excess of 18 million, also leading to Jones collecting eight Grammy awards.

The hugely anticipated follow-up album, *Feels Like Home*, was released in 2004, again proving to be a big hit as it offered yet further takes on Norah's eclectic mix of blues, country and piano-based jazz.

Come Away With Me

Words and Music by Norah Jones

Backing

Waltz (with a country swing feel) ♩ = 184

Come a - way— with me— in the night.—

Come a - way— with me— and I will— write— you— a

in fields___ where the yel-low grass grows___ knee___ high so won't you___ try___ to

come. Come a-way___ with me___ and we'll kiss on a moun-tain top.___

Come a-way___ with me___ and I'll___ nev-er stop lov-ing

you.

Don't Miss You At All

Words and Music by Norah Jones and Duke Ellington

Don't Know Why

Words and Music by Jesse Harris

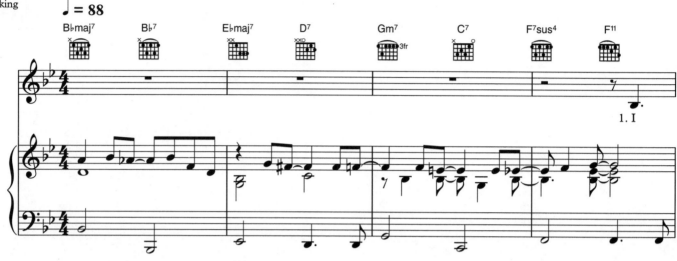

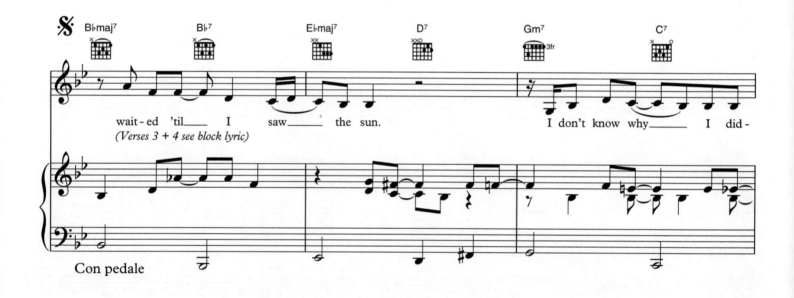

3. Out across the endless sea
   I will die in ecstasy
   but I'll be a bag of bones
   Driving down the road alone.

   My heart is drenched in wine etc.

4. Something has to make you run
   I don't know why I didn't come
   I feel as empty as a drum
   I don't know why I didn't come
   I don't know why I didn't come
   I don't know why I didn't come.

Feelin' The Same Way

Words and Music by Lee Alexander

1. The sun just slipped its note be-low my door,— and I can't hide be-neath— my
2. An-oth-er day that I— can't find my— head,— my feet don't look like they're— my
(Verse 3 see block lyric)

— sheets.— I've read the words— be-fore,— so now I know—
— own.— I'll try and find— the floor— be-low to stand,—

ov - er a - gain,___ no mat - ter how much I pre - tend, no

mat - ter how much I pre - tend. Ah.___

Ah.___

rit.

Verse 3:
So many times I wonder where I've gone
And how I found my way back in
I look around a while for something lost
Maybe I'll find it in the end

And I'm feelin' the same way *etc.*

Nightingale

Words and Music by Norah Jones

Painter Song

Words and Music by Lee Alexander and J. C. Hopkins

Track 6
Backing

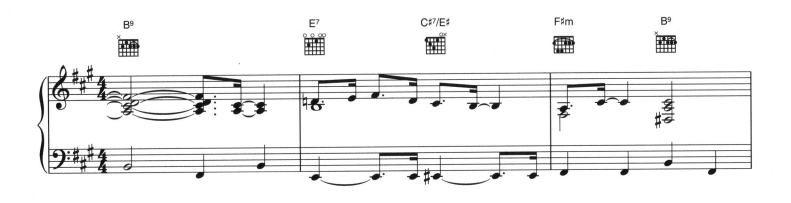

1. If I were a paint - er,___ I would paint my re - ver -
- ge - ther___ just___ like we___ used to
(Verse 3 instrumental until *)

The Prettiest Thing

Words and Music by Norah Jones, Lee Alexander and Richard Julian

Sunrise

Words and Music by Norah Jones and Lee Alexander

Those Sweet Words

Words and Music by Lee Alexander and Richard Julian

What Am I To You?

Words and Music by Norah Jones

YOU'RE THE VOICE

8861A PV/CD

Casta Diva from Norma – Vissi D'arte from Tosca – Un Bel Di Vedremo from Madama Butterfly – Addio, Del Passato from La Traviata – J'ai Perdu Mon Eurydice from Orphee Et Eurydice – Les Tringles Des Sistres Tintaient from Carmen – Porgi Amor from Le Nozze Di Figaro – Ave Maria from Otello

8860A PVG/CD

Delilah – Green Green Grass Of Home – Help Yourself – I'll Never Fall In Love Again – It's Not Unusual – Mama Told Me Not To Come – Sexbomb – Thunderball – What's New Pussycat – You Can Leave Your Hat On

9297A PVG/CD

Beauty And The Beast – Because You Loved Me – Falling Into You – The First Time Ever I Saw Your Face – It's All Coming Back To Me Now – Misled – My Heart Will Go On – The Power Of Love – Think Twice – When I Fall In Love

9349A PVG/CD

Chain Of Fools – A Deeper Love Do Right Woman, Do Right Man – I Knew You Were Waiting (For Me) – I Never Loved A Man (The Way I Loved You) – I Say A Little Prayer – Respect – Think – Who's Zooming Who – (You Make Me Feel Like) A Natural Woman

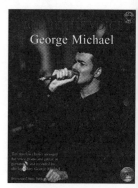

9007A PVG/CD

Careless Whisper – A Different Corner – Faith – Father Figure – Freedom '90 – I'm Your Man – I Knew You Were Waiting (For Me) – Jesus To A Child – Older – Outside

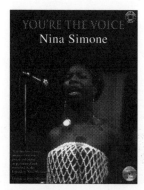

9606A PVG/CD

Don't Let Me Be Misunderstood – Feeling Good – I Loves You Porgy – I Put A Spell On You – Love Me Or Leave Me – Mood Indigo – My Baby Just Cares For Me – Ne Me Quitte Pas (If You Go Away) – Nobody Knows You When You're Down And Out – Take Me To The Water

9700A PVG/CD

Beautiful – Crying In The Rain – I Feel The Earth Move – It's Too Late – (You Make Me Feel Like) A Natural Woman – So Far Away – Way Over Yonder – Where You Lead – Will You Love Me Tomorrow – You've Got A Friend

9746A PVG/CD

April In Paris – Come Rain Or Come Shine – Fly Me To The Moon (In Other Words) – I've Got You Under My Skin – The Lady Is A Tramp – My Kinda Town (Chicago Is) – My Way – Theme From *New York, New York* – Someone To Watch Over Me – Something Stupid

9770A PVG/CD

Cry Me A River – Evergreen (A Star Is Born) – Happy Days Are Here Again – I've Dreamed Of You – Memory – My Heart Belongs To Me – On A Clear Day (You Can See Forever) – Someday My Prince Will Come – Tell Him (duet with Celine Dion) – The Way We Were

9799A PVG/CD

Boogie Woogie Bugle Boy – Chapel Of Love – Friends – From A Distance – Hello In There – One For My Baby (And One More For The Road) – Only In Miami – The Rose – When A Man Loves A Woman – Wind Beneath My Wings

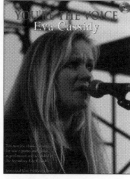

9810A PVG/CD

Ain't No Sunshine – Autumn Leaves – How Can I Keep From Singing – Imagine – It Doesn't Matter Anymore – Over The Rainbow – Penny To My Name – People Get Ready – Wayfaring Stranger – What A Wonderful World

9889A PVG/CD

Around The World – Born Free – From Russia With Love – Gonna Build A Mountain – The Impossible Dream – My Kind Of Girl – On A Clear Day You Can See Forever – Portrait Of My Love – Softly As I Leave You – Walk Away

10039A PVG/CD

All Of Me – Body And Soul – God Bless The Child – I Love My Man ('Billie's Blues') – Lady Sings The Blues – Lover Man (Oh Where Can You Be) – The Man I Love – My Man ('Mon Homme') – Night And Day – St. Louis Blues

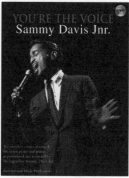

10091A PVG/CD

For Once In My Life – Hey There – It's All Right With Me – I've Gotta Be Me – Let's Face The Music And Dance – Love Me Or Leave Me – Mr Bojangles – September Song – Something's Gotta Give – What Kind Of Fool Am I?

10119A PVG/CD

Come Away With Me – Don't Know Why – Don't Miss You At All – Feelin' The Same Way – Nightingale – Painter Song – The Prettiest Thing – Sunrise – Those Sweet Words – What Am I To You?

The outstanding vocal series from IMP

CD contains full backings for each song, professionally arranged to recreate the sounds of the original recording